Usborne

Wipe-Clean Phonics

Book 4

Written by Mairi Mackinnon
Illustrated by Fred Blunt

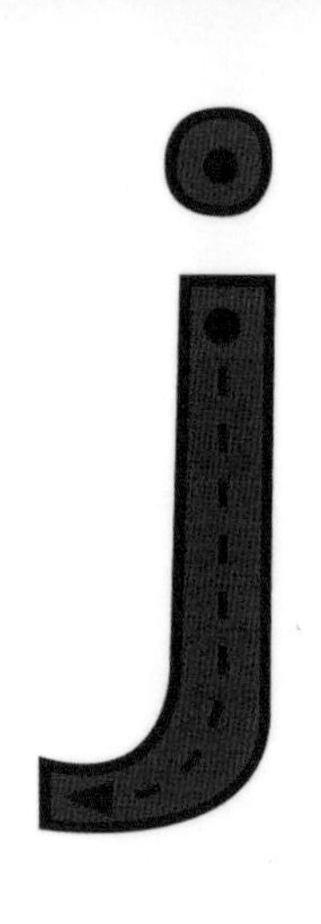

Say the sound: j-j-j-j

Write a big **j** in the air with your finger, then do it on the page.

Trace over this **j** with your pen.

Circle all the things that begin with **j**.

Write a **j** next to the things that start with **j**.

Jaguar jazz

Down in the jungle, the jaguars are jamming.

Trace the j with your pen and write some more.

These jolly jellyfish are jiggling and jumping about in the warm ocean current.

Finish their tentacles with j shapes.

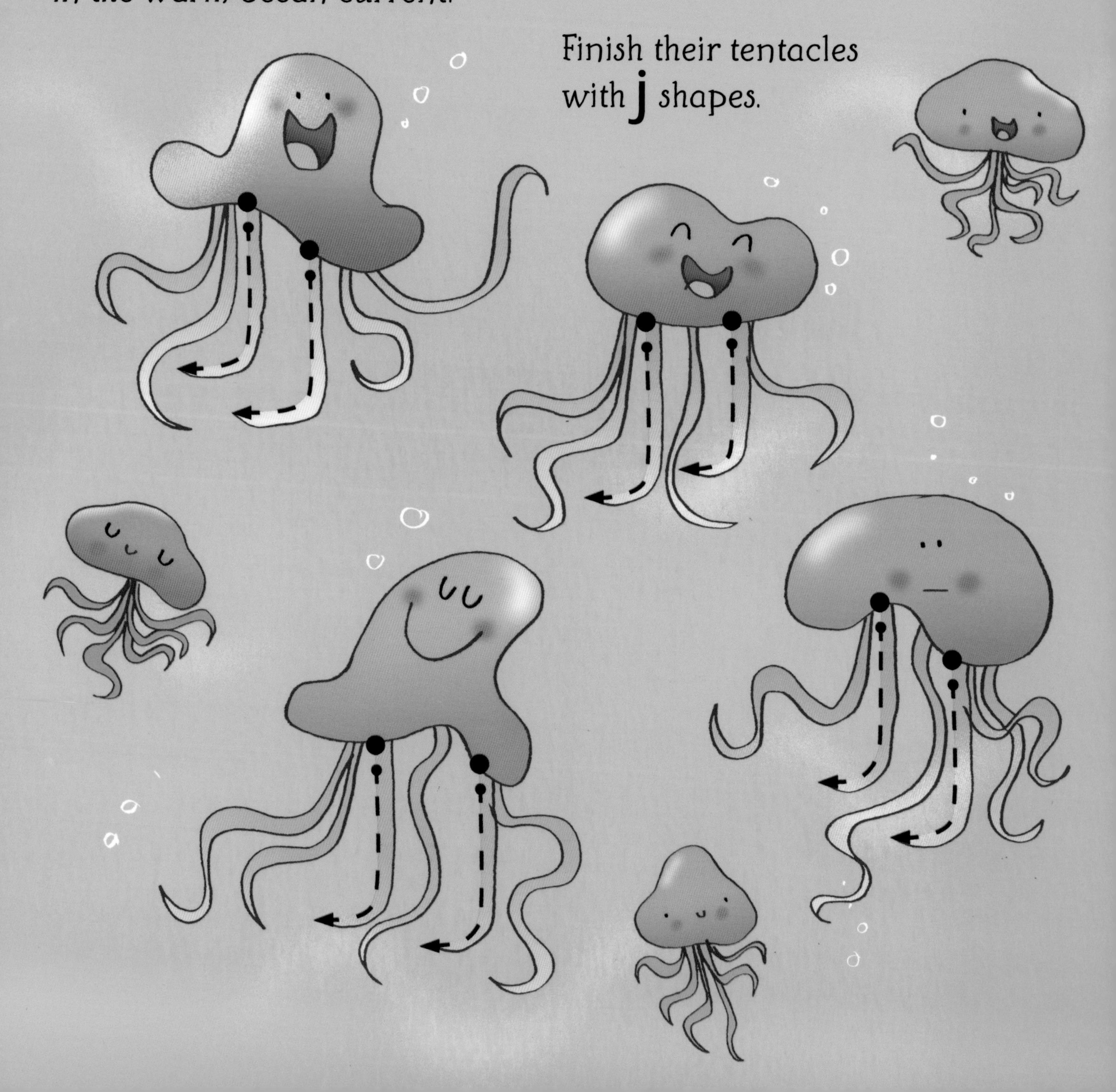

Say the sound: qu-qu-qu

Write a big **q** in the air with your finger, then again on the page.

Trace over this **q** with your pen.

Not many things begin with **q**.

Can you find one? Draw a circle around it.

Write a **q** next to the thing that starts with **q**.

Quirky queens

There are quite a lot of queens here!
Can you find:

- a queen under a quilt
- some queens quarrelling
- some queens queuing?

Write **q** in the circle next to them.

Can you spot anything else that begins with **q**?

Trace the **q** with your pen and write some more.

Quentin the quizmaster is asking some seriously tricky questions.

Finish drawing everyone's faces using **q** shapes.

Making words

Put **j - e - t** together and you get **jet**.

Read the letters. Read the word. Now write it.

j e t jet jet

What do you get if you put **j - o - g** together?

j o g jog jog

How about **qu - i - ck**?

qu i ck quick

Which of these pictures is right for jet? Write **jet** underneath.

1

2

3

Which of these is right for jog? Write **jog** under it.

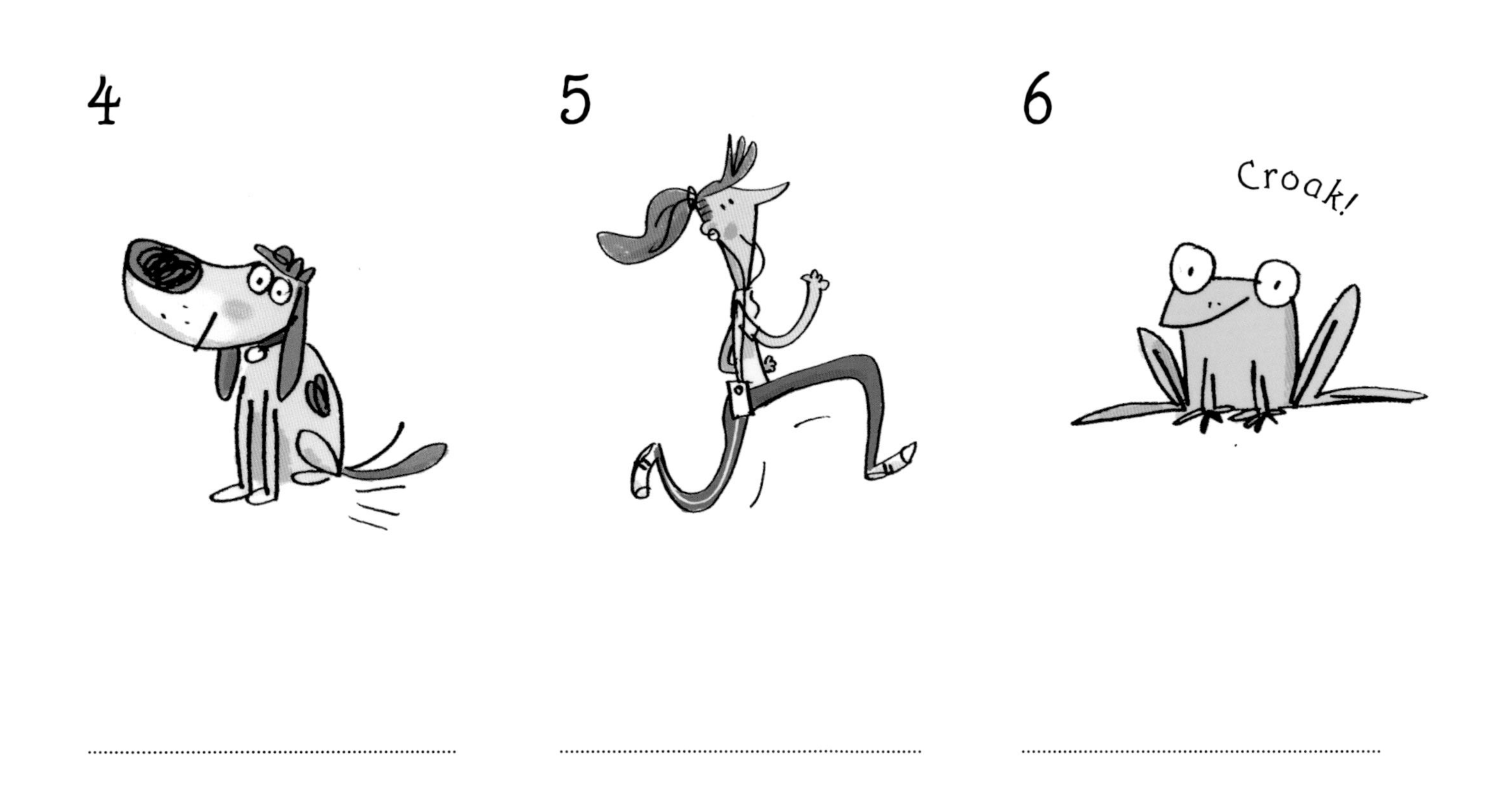

Which one is right for quick? Write **quick** under it.

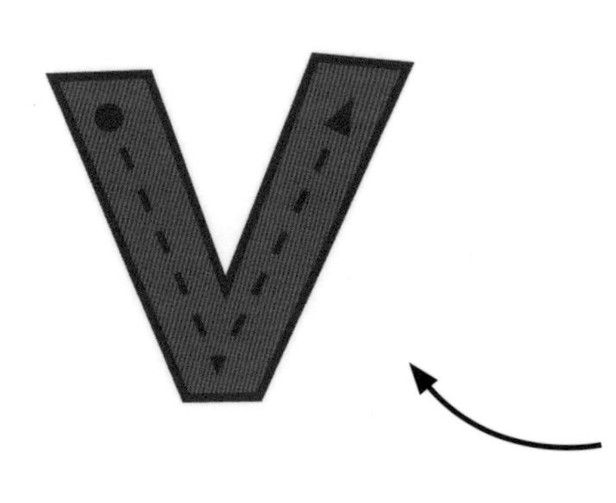

Say the sound: v-v-v-v

Write a big **V** in the air with your finger, then on this page.

Trace over this big **V** with your pen.

Draw a circle around all the things that begin with **V**.

Try writing **V** next to the things that start with **V**.

Say the sound: w-w-w-w

Write a big **W** in the air with your finger, then do it again on this page.

Trace over this big **W** with your pen, starting at the dot.

Draw a circle around all the things that begin with **W**.

Write **W** next to the things that start with **W**.

Wasps welcome

These wasps don't want to waste all this food that the humans have left, so they're having a picnic in the sun.

Draw around their zigzag markings using **W** shapes.

Trace the **w** with your pen and write some more.

w w w

Wow! Don't Woody and Wendy look wonderful on their wedding day?

Finish all the collars, and also the bows on Wendy's dress, using **w** shapes.

Making words

Put **v - a - n** together and you get **van**.

Read the letters. Read the word. Now write it.

v a n van van

What do you get if you put **v - e - t** together?

v e t vet vet

How about **w - e - ll**?

w e ll well well

Which of these pictures is right for van? Write **van** under it.

1

2

3

Which of these pictures is right for vet? Write **vet** under it.

Which of these is right for well? Write **well** under it.

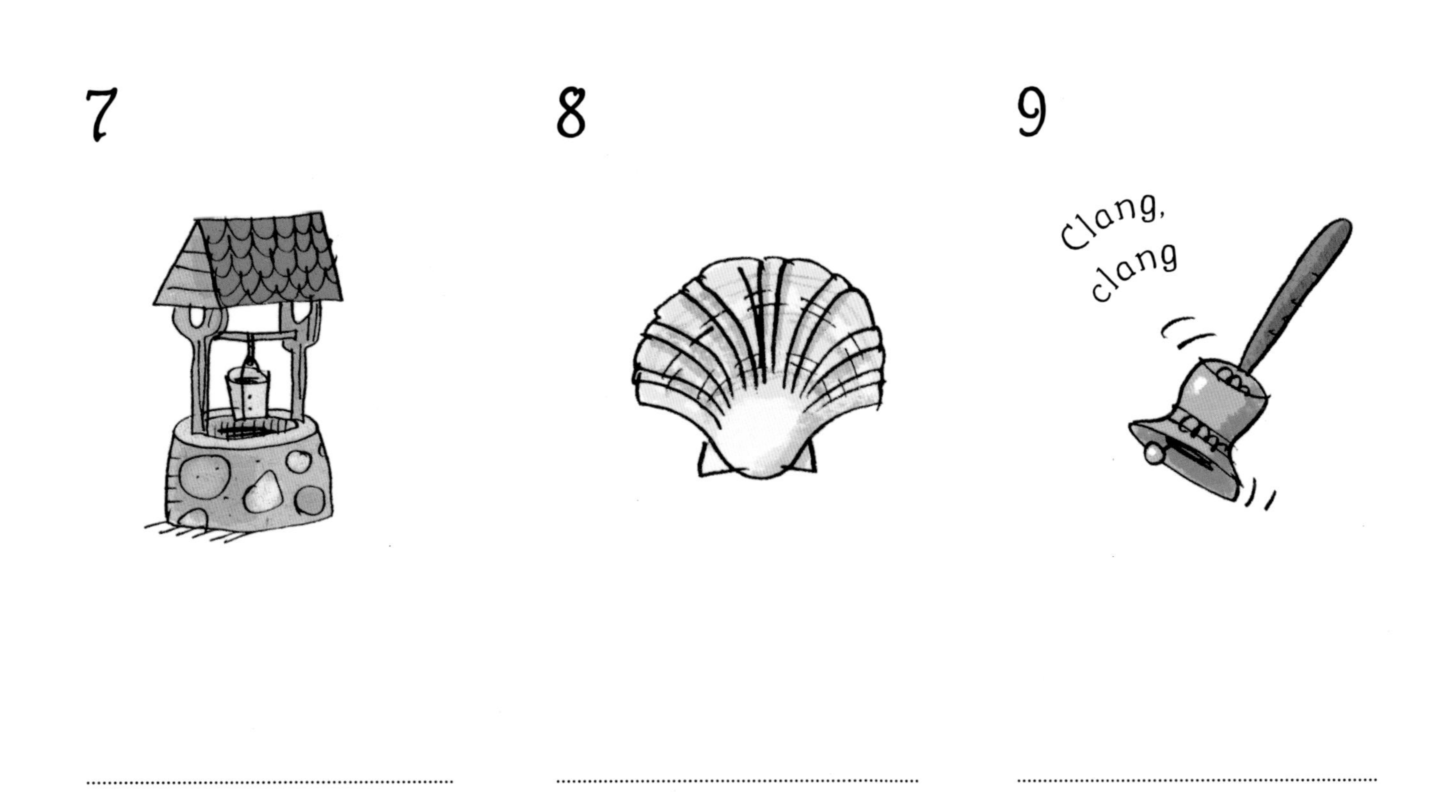

Say the sound: x-x-x-x

Write a big **X** in the air with your finger, then do it again on this page.

Trace over this big **X** with your pen, starting at the dot.

X is often found in the middle or at the end of a word.

Draw a circle around the things that end with **X.**

Write an **X** next to all the things that end with **X.**

Foxes with boxes

It's Alex Fox's birthday, and her friends have brought stacks of presents. Felix Fox is more interested in eating the cake, though!

Finish the presents by drawing **X**-shaped ribbons on the boxes.

Mmm!

Oooh!

Trace the **X** with your pen and write some more.

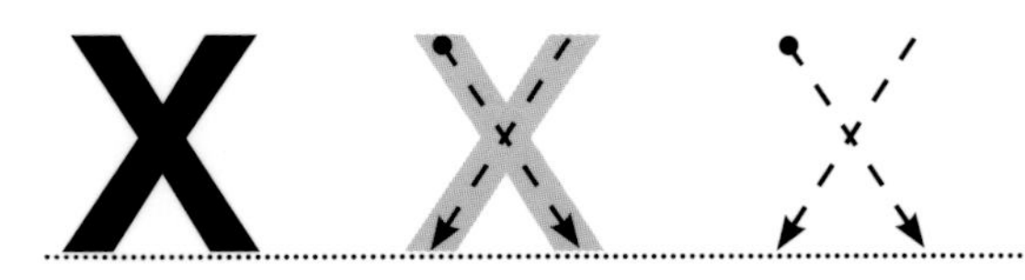

These three absent-minded pirates have forgotten where they buried their treasure! Help them to find the hiding places on the map below, and draw **X**s to mark the spots.

Can you see any more **X** shapes on the map?

Say the sound: y-y-y-y

Write a big **y** in the air with your finger, then on the page.

Trace around this big **y** with your pen, keeping the pen on the page.

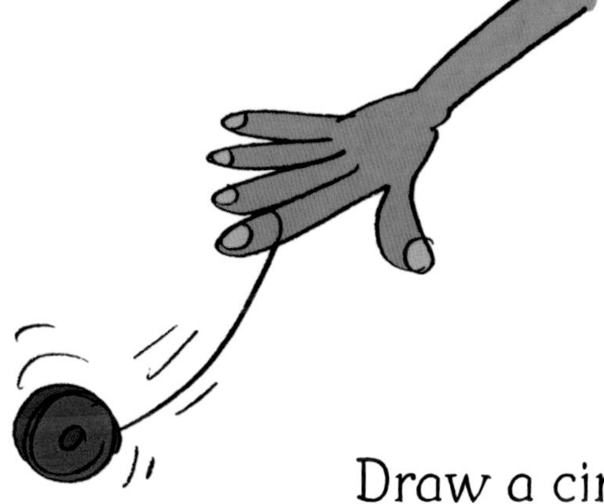

Draw a circle around all the things that begin with **y**.

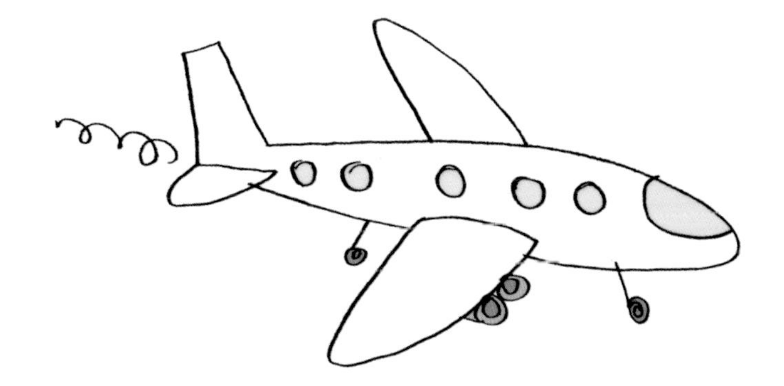

Write **y** next to the things that start with **y**.

The yak pack

Yikes, there are yaks everywhere!
Can you write a **y** next to:

- a yak with a yo-yo
- a yak doing yoga
- a yak with a yacht
- a yak yawning?

Can you spot any more things that begin with a **y**?

Trace the **y** with your pen and write some more.

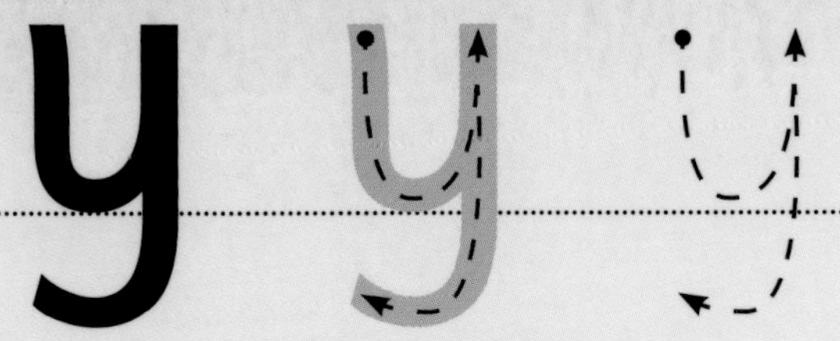

High in the Himalayas, this mountaineer has made a startling discovery.

Finish drawing the yelling yetis' mouths using **y** shapes.

Making words

Put **b - o - x** together and you get **box**.

Read the letters. Read the word. Now write it.

b o x box box

What do you get if you put **m - i - x** together?

m i x mix mix

How about **y - e - ll**?

y e ll yell yell

Which of these pictures is right for box? Write **box** under it.

1 

2 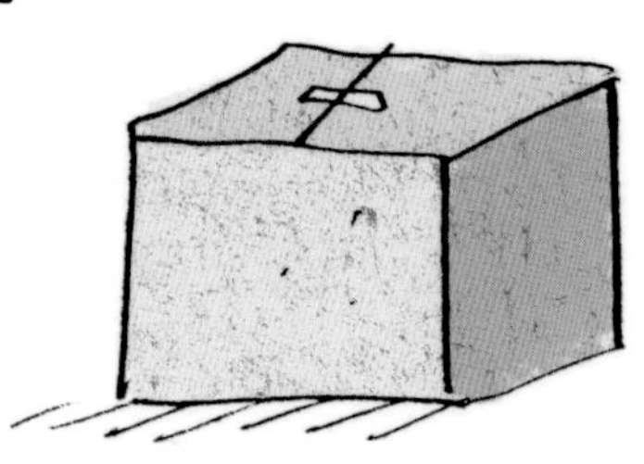

3 

Which of these is right for mix? Write **mix** under it.

Which one is right for yell? Write **yell** under it.

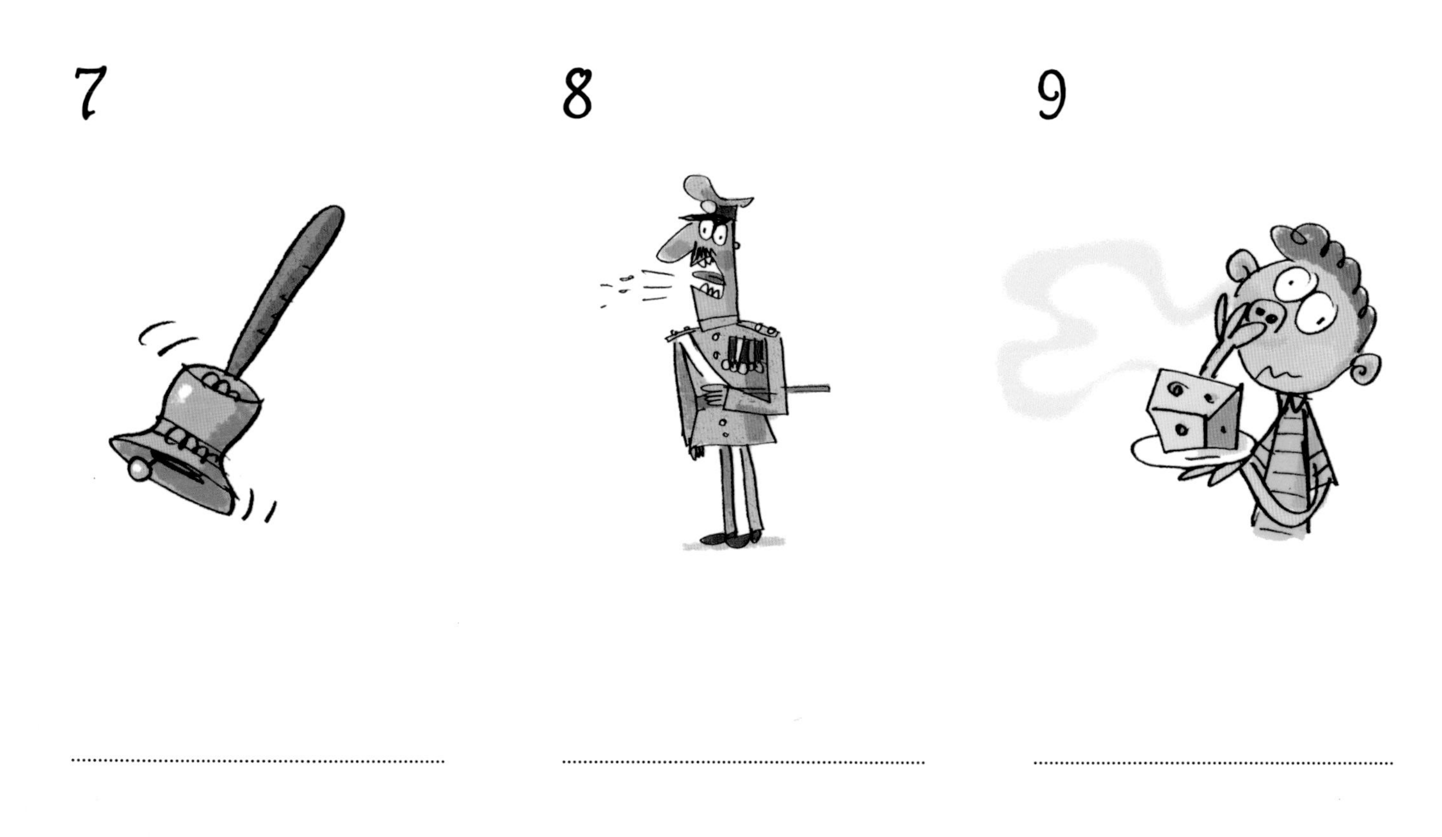

Say the sound: zzzz

Write a big **Z** in the air with your finger, then on the page.

Trace over this big **Z**, starting at the dot.

Draw a circle around all the things that begin with **Z.**

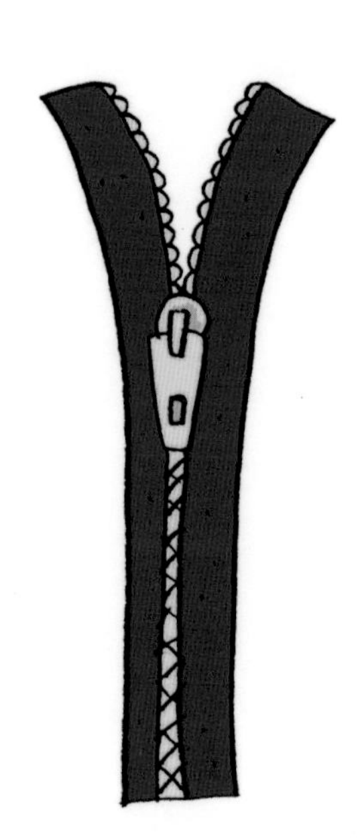

Try writing **Z** next to the things that start with **Z.**

Stormy night

It's a wild and dangerous night to be out at sea. Finish drawing the zigzag lightning zapping down from the clouds.

Trace the **Z** with your pen and write some more.

Z Z Z

Zoe, Zac, Zander and Zara are performing their big opening number at the talent show.

Finish drawing their legs with **Z** shapes.

Say the sound: zzzzzz

Trace over this big **zz** with your pen.

Draw around all the things that make a **zz** sound.

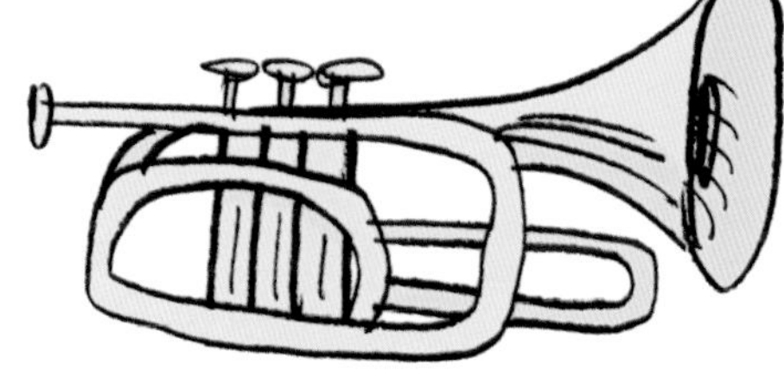

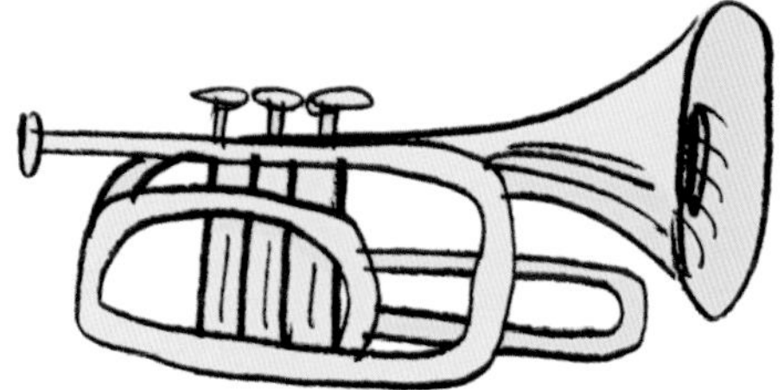

Write **zz** next to the things that make a **zz** sound.

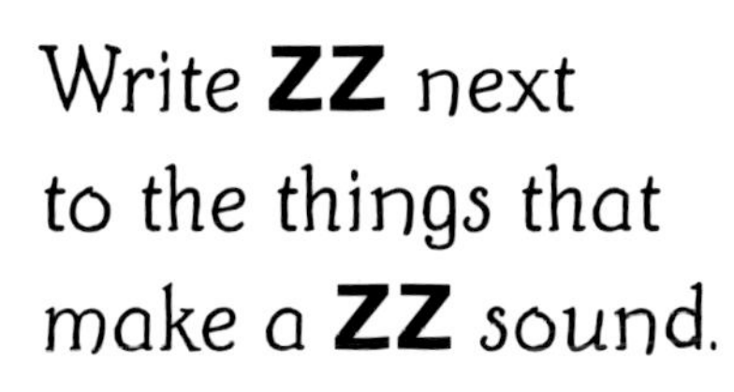

Snoozing at the zoo

It's a warm summer afternoon, and all the zoo animals are dozing off in the heat.

Buzzzzz

Write **ZZ**s next to the sleeping creatures.

Capital letters and small letters

You use capital letters at the beginning of a name or sentence.
Trace and then copy these letters. Start with the dotted line.

Volcano valley

This happy dinosaur mother has four new babies. Draw around the spikes on her back and the broken eggshells using **V** shapes.

Trace the **V** with your pen and write some more.

Victor, Vernon and Vincent the vampires are on their way out for the evening.

Draw their fangs using **V** shapes.